PRIDE'S PROGRESS

Harper & Row, Publishers   New York and Evanston

PRIDE'S PROGRESS

THE STORY OF A FAMILY OF LIONS

To Thilde and Eva

ACKNOWLEDGMENTS

Slender as this book appears, it owes its existence to help from many quarters. I am most grateful to the New York Zoological Society for extending innumerable courtesies to me in my inquiry and picture taking.

Above all, I am indebted to Mr. Joseph A. Davis, Jr., Curator of Mammals, New York Zoological Society until the end of December, 1966, for his constant encouragement, his keen interest, his invaluable advice and suggestions, and the assistance most generously given. Without him this book would not have come about. He most graciously volunteered to draw the map of the African Plains exhibit and surrounding area that appear on page viii. He was also kind enough to correct the manuscript, and read it before it went to press.

I want to express my warmest thanks to Mr. William Bridges, Curator of Publications of the New York Zoological Society, now retired, who has always looked upon my picture taking with benevolent interest, and has given me much help.

My heartfelt appreciation goes to Dr. James W. Atz, Associate Curator, Department of Ichthyology, American Museum of Natural History, who started me on the road to attempting photo books on animals when he was Curator at the New York Aquarium. He also obtained for me a reading list on lion behavior from the Mammal Department of the American Museum of Natural History.

Furthermore, I acknowledge with gratitude the help extended to me by the following officials and employees of the New York Zoological Society: Mr. John A. Miller, Associate Curator of Publications; Mr. H. Bradford House, Assistant Curator of Mammals; Mrs. Dorothy Reville, Editorial Assistant; Miss Lucy Long; Head Keeper Joseph Ruff, Department of Mammals; and Senior Keeper Roy Hosmer and Keeper Warren Lawston, who had the daily care of the lions described in this book and very kindly assisted me on countless occasions.

CONTENTS

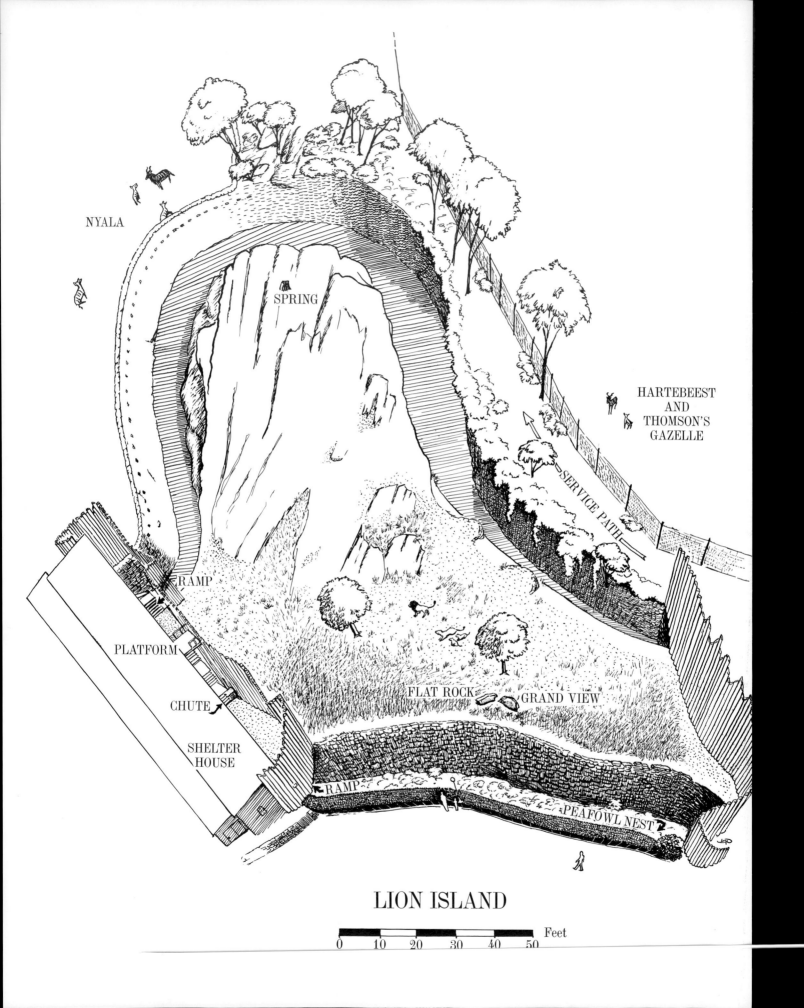

NYALA

SPRING

HARTEBEEST
AND
THOMSON'S
GAZELLE

SERVICE PATH

RAMP

PLATFORM

CHUTE

SHELTER
HOUSE

FLAT ROCK

GRAND VIEW

RAMP

PEAFOWL NEST

LION ISLAND

Feet

0   10   20   30   40   50

INTRODUCTION

In modern times various naturalists have attempted a coup against the King of
Beasts. If they have not quite succeeded in toppling his throne in the public eye
they have at least managed to portray him as an indolent despot whose wives do
all the work and who simply takes the lion's share of the kill, gluts himself, and
then indulges himself in a long postprandial siesta under a shady tree. There is
an element of half-truth in these revelations of the lion's rather human foibles,
and a half-truth can often be misleading.

The lion is not a conventional cat. It has been said that he is a dog in cat's
clothing, and in truth his psychological makeup *is* doglike, in that, alone among
the cats, he prefers to live a social existence in a family group called a "pride."
No really intimate study of the life within a pride has ever been made, and
Emmy Haas's observations throw a revealing light on what goes on within a
royal family. She shows the admirable and majestic side of the lion's domestic
life—without covering up the fact that even a king may sometimes lose patience
with the exuberance of his children. As Miss Haas points out, this is the true
story of one lion, Charlie, one lioness, Princess, and their offspring. Their
behavior may not always be true of lions in the wild, nor even of all zoo lions;
there just isn't enough known about lions yet for us to tell. Still, her narrative
gives us a glimpse of that side of the lion's nature that is in keeping with the
older view of the King of Beasts, and I suspect that when good detailed field
studies have been made they will show the Bronx Zoo lions to have been more
typical of their species than we dare admit today.

I need only add that what began simply as a photographic project has led Miss
Haas to delve deeply into the literature on lions and, more importantly, to focus
not only her camera but her powers of observation on the young pride of lions
in the zoo. The results are the fascinating and beautiful photographs in this book,
and the no less fascinating verbal portraits of the lions and their family life—
of the happenings that most zoo visitors never pause long enough to see.

JOSEPH A. DAVIS, JR.

FOREWORD

This book is the result of several years of lion watching at the New York Zoological Park's African Plains exhibit.

In photographing the behavior of these lions, my aim, at first, was merely to put together a picture record of the activities of these fascinating animals. Soon afterward I began searching for reliable literature on many facets of lion behavior that had astounded me while I observed these animals from across the moat or some other vantage point. I had hoped that I would find these discussed by a knowledgeable biologist, but this quest proved unsuccessful. Nor did I find good photographic sequences of a lion family's life among themselves in any of the books and periodicals that I encountered. The scarcity of literature on this topic was confirmed to me by a few people, and a statement by L. S. B. Leakey in the introduction to Ylla's book *Animals in Africa* (1953) seems to bear this out, for he deplored the fact that the behavior of the wild animals in Africa had never been studied at length. A few zoologists have since started on such endeavors.

Lions are the only truly social cats in existence. They live in prides, i.e., family groups, that vary greatly in size and composition depending on abundance of game, territorial pressure, predatory incursions by man, and the personalities of the animals involved. However, some aspects concerning the formation of prides are still not completely understood. Information about lion territories differs, probably because the various observers covered different regions at different times and under widely varying circumstances. The size of a lion's territory does seem to be quite closely related to the abundance of game, availability of water, and whether or not the animal lives in a pride. It seems that territories of prides may even overlap to a degree without leading to serious quarrels between the lionesses involved, as long as enough game is available, for apparently to a lioness a territory is merely a hunting ground. For a male lion, however, a territory must also hold a certain number of lionesses ready to mate with him from time to time. Therefore his territory may encompass the hunting grounds of various prides and single lionesses, and thus extend over a sizable range.

The writers of many books, articles, and reports give only fragmentary (sometimes tantalizing) glimpses of lion behavior in their natural habitat because time has permitted only occasional visits to study these animals. C. A. W. Guggisberg has not only written a classic on these amazing creatures but has also spent a considerable portion of his life in Africa and untold hours with the big cats. During innumerable visits over long periods, he was able to learn a great deal about the fate of one pride and some of the cubs that grew up in it. His observations are fascinating and very helpful. Yet he had to interrupt his field studies at times for shorter or longer periods because of his duties at the Medical Research Laboratory in Nairobi. Joy Adamson has given us a wonderful and astonishing account of Elsa the lioness and her cubs, but their life, as recorded by her, did not include the male who sired Elsa's cubs, and the description of Elsa and her young centered, of necessity, around the Adamsons' household and therefore did not reveal the displays that occur between animals without such close human attachments.

It is quite apparent that lion watching in Africa is infinitely more difficult than observing some animals from across a moat in the Bronx Zoo, particularly if you aim to find out something about their behavior within a group. This is, of course, one of the reasons why zoological parks have been invaluable as places of careful record keeping and essential research. They have been prominent in gathering and imparting information on the physical makeup, habits, and behavior of a great many species about which hardly anything was known before they were maintained in zoos.

EMMY HAAS

New York City
November, 1966

CHARLIE
AND
PRINCESS

The lions in this book never roamed the vast plains of Africa. They are confined to the African Plains exhibit at the Bronx Zoo, and in particular to Lion Island, a rocky, triangular piece of land, about fifty feet at its base and some sixty-five feet at each side. The island is almost surrounded by a deep moat, and there is a low shelter house along one corner; the animals are confined to the shelter building overnight and during inclement weather. There are two rock outcroppings facing the viewer from across the moat, one of them rather low and of even height, called Flat Rock, the other one, right next to it, called Grandview Rock. Both of these rocks are about ten feet away from the brink.

Charlie

Princess

Charlie, the male, and Princess, his mate, have been living on this island since 1960. The New York Zoological Society acquired the former in January 1959, when he was about five months old, and obtained Princess in May 1960; her age was then estimated to be around fifteen months. Charlie had been raised at the National Zoological Park in Washington, while Princess had come to the Bronx Zoo through an animal dealer. Nowadays, zoo lions are, with few exceptions, no longer imported into the United States from Africa, but are raised in this country, the offspring of zoo or circus animals.

Thus Charlie and Princess were still youngsters when they were put on the island, and a thin wire strung around part of the brink served to put them on notice that there was a dangerous edge, so that they would not topple into the moat unexpectedly and injure themselves. For in years past, when the Zoo exhibited only male lions on the island, two newly arrived cubs, about a year old, were lost from spinal injuries sustained in falls into the moat from an island with whose topography they had been unfamiliar.

The wire has long since been removed. And Princess and Charlie take good care that none of their cubs fall into the moat. On one of the earliest outings of Princess's and Charlie's first litter, I saw Charlie run after one of his cubs and push it back to safety with a swipe of his tremendous paw after it had strayed dangerously close to the edge and had given us, who were watching, a very bad scare.

When Charlie first came to Lion Island, he did not yet have the magnificent mane he now possesses. Now his long thick mane covers his shoulders, and he has dark elbow tufts and a dark belly fringe. He is in his prime. Princess, too, has reached her full growth, but being a female, she has kept her juvenile coat except that the spots cubs are generally covered with have faded somewhat. When the light hits her from a certain angle, though, these spots seem fairly pronounced, even now, and as photographic emulsions are very sensitive to these slight color variations, the rosettes show up distinctly on many of my photographs.

Charlie may look majestic to a human eye, but this impression is misleading.
Both he and Princess are quite playful, and one day, toward the end of
September 1963, when the weather was pleasant and cool, Charlie showed
Princess plainly that he wanted to play with her by catching hold of her a few
times as she passed him and by rolling on the ground and looking at her while

lying there, stretched out. Princess did not disappoint him. She walked up to Charlie. He reached for her, pulled her close, drew her head down with his arm, fondled and licked her, and when she was about to sit down next to him, he pulled her over, upsetting her. Both seemed to enjoy rolling about on their backs with their feet up in the air.

Princess and Charlie appear to observe all the niceties and formalities of proper
lion behavior. They are devoted to each other, to be sure, but like all male lions,
Charlie needs more privacy than his partner, and he will frequently sit somewhat
apart from his mate. Princess respects his preference, but she will not have him
sit alone for any length of time without walking over to him every so often to
rub her head against his, and he always responds in kind. Sometimes she will
then return to where she had been sitting, but occasionally she seems to desire
his companionship and may eventually stretch out close to him. This often
repeated greeting ceremony is an integral part of lion behavior and has
frequently been observed by naturalists in the field, not only among members of
one pride, but also when groups of apparently friendly—or related?—lions meet
each other in the wild. Our African Plains lions indulge in it for several
minutes every morning as they rejoin each other out on the island after having
been separated during the night.

A few years ago there was a fine scratching post on Lion Island, and both Charlie and Princess used it frequently, although Princess seemed partial also to the wood-covered wall of the shelter house, which gave her an equal opportunity to stand up, sharpen her claws, and stretch legs and back at the same time. One day Princess spotted Charlie at that post and walked over to him; while he was industriously exercising his huge claws, she stood up against the post, and it looked as if they were having a very sociable time together.

From the beginning, Charlie and Princess proved to be a wonderful show, for they got along together very well, were delightfully playful, and are a very handsome pair of lions, greatly devoted to each other.

FIRST CUB

A lion's gestation period has been established by authorities as lasting from 100 to 113 days. Our lions' first litter of cubs was born in January 1962 and consisted of one female and one male. Charlie met these cubs when they were still quite small and confined to the shelter house. I was told that, not having had any previous experience with little cubs, Charlie was quite rough with them and batted them about, and Princess had neither sense nor experience enough to interfere. Therefore Charlie was banished from the nursery until the cubs were sturdier. Their first outings on the island had taken place without their sire. Consequently staff members and zoo personnel were curious—and on hand—to witness Charlie's reaction on seeing his cubs on the island for the first time. Sure enough, when Charlie spotted his youngsters he came right over and cuffed one of them, much to everybody's concern, until it was noticed that instead of running away, the victim came back for more. When Princess felt that the game was getting out of hand, she squirmed in between her cub and Charlie, and as Charlie is—and was then—very attached to Princess, her nearness made him forget his cub, and he had eyes only for his mate.

Unfortunately, I did not watch the first-litter cubs regularly. In fact, I observed them so seldom that I was never able to tell them apart while they were small. (It is, of course, easy to do so when cubs are older.) Therefore I am repeating what I have heard about their ''social life'' from Mr. Joseph A. Davis, Jr., Curator of Mammals at the Zoo during that time, and from their keepers. They all told me that the little female was partial to Charlie, and that the little male favored Princess.

To everybody's dismay both of these first two cubs developed calcium deficiencies, for which were duly treated. But the Zoo felt that it would be preferable for sturdier cubs to form the nucleus of a pride, and so, after the cubs had recovered, they were given away when they were about one to one-and-a-half years of age.

MORE CUBS

Cass nursing, Polly between her parents

On August 1, 1963, Princess had her second litter—a male, Cass, and a female, Polly. For months I wondered why the cubs had been given these names, but was reluctant to ask as it seemed too trivial a matter. The answer was presented to me one day almost by accident. It appeared that they had originally been named for the Gemini, Castor and Pollux; their names were then shortened to Cass and Polly.

In zoos, lion cubs are generally kept indoors with their mother for the first
several weeks of their lives, for lion mothers are very protective of
their young and want a great deal of privacy for them. When Cass
and Polly were about six weeks of age, Princess took them out on the
island for short periods, and after another week or so, Charlie met
them for the first time out of doors. In comparison with his earliest
encounter with the cubs of the previous litter, Charlie was very gentle
with his new babies, and gave Polly just a few exploratory pokes with
his paw while Princess looked on benignly. Even at that age, certain
differences between the little cubs were very striking: Polly had a
decidedly darker coat than her brother, who appeared unusually
blond. After this introduction to their father, the youngsters explored
the clumps of grass and a few boulders in their immediate vicinity,
while both parents followed them around dutifully.

From the beginning Polly seemed to prefer her father while Cass wanted to be with his mother. Polly used to play endlessly with Charlie's tail, and the scene often reminded me of Mr. Davis's remark that it is hard to watch a lion with his cubs and not believe that the tail tuft is really there for his cubs to play with. The cubs appeared to share this view. Charlie had to change positions frequently in order to get this prominent but vulnerable toy out of the way of his playful little daughter, for she enjoyed clamping down on it with her teeth. Sometimes, however, she only cuddled his tail without hurting him, and then the onlooker was rewarded with the sight of Charlie looking sublimely contented.

Apparently, a lion's coat is a good protection against the tweaking these animals sometimes have to endure from their small cubs' sharp little teeth. For Polly seemed to enjoy nipping Charlie, and Cass did the same to Princess, and yet both parents responded by merely turning their heads and giving their cubs benevolent looks. They never reproved their youngsters when they were rough, and were most tolerant parents.

Princess is an excellent mother. When the cubs were tiny and ventured too far for her liking, or when she became anxious for their safety because of a whirring movie camera or a threatening long lens, she walked over to the cub she felt needed protection, took its head between her jaws and carried it to safety. Or she would very unceremoniously grab her baby by the rump to seek a secure place for it.

For the same reason Princess wanted Cass and Polly to remain in view when they were very small. But once Cass had other ideas. He was as determined to crawl through the cleft between Flat Rock and Grandview as his mother was in keeping him on the near side of these rocks. First she nudged him away from the cleft with her paw, but he persisted in trying to creep through. Next she put her foot down on him, quite literally, to make him stay put. Then she caught him by his paw and attempted to carry him away. It did not work. Patiently, she continued trying to catch hold of him and carry him to a safer place, but when she had him by his hind leg, he merely rested his weight against the rock. She finally gave up and escorted him away, all the time talking to him softly.

Later on the cub frightened her by sitting too close to the edge of the moat, whereupon she caught him by his ear, probably to pull him away, and he wailed loudly in protest.

At times the little cubs played quietly around Princess. On one occasion Cass was most anxious to catch a branch of the vine that dangled in front of his face, and when he reached across Princess's chest, she took this as an invitation to lick him.

The cubs, at that stage, still appeared quite helpless. For occasionally Princess was stopped in her tracks by a wailing cub that had found it too difficult to catch up with mother, so that she would either go over and lick and comfort her cub or else wait for her baby.

Late in September 1963, the edge of the moat was found in need of repairs. Until this had been attended to, the little cubs were kept indoors while the adults were out on the island, as it was feared that the youngsters might get hurt if they were permitted out of doors. Princess walked over to the shelter house innumerable times in the course of those days to listen intently for the sounds of her cubs inside.

The cubs were allowed back on the island at the beginning of October, and it was striking to see how much they had grown in this very short period and how much more independent they had become. They were most amusing as they romped together and pawed each other; in fact, now you could really watch them disport themselves, whereas a few weeks earlier they had disappeared from view each time they had sat down or stretched out where the grass was somewhat tall. It was also interesting to see that they seemed to have more staying power than they had a few weeks earlier. At that time they had to lie down to recover from their

exertions after very short periods of activity. Now they seemed to rest after longer intervals. They still trooped over to Princess quite frequently and lined up against her body to nurse. As soon as she saw them playing close to the brink, Princess, watchful as ever, would follow her cubs to sit alert on the edge of the dangerous steep drops into the moat to shield her youngsters from accidents.

A few weeks later I noticed Cass for the first time watching his mother at the scratching post as she flexed the muscles to bare her claws. Afterward he jumped

Cass being groomed

up against the post himself, without, apparently, quite knowing what her action had been about. On that day, too, the cubs managed to climb Flat Rock, and they looked very proud of this achievement. They had a wonderful time playing King of the Castle with Polly atop, until Princess came along for a game with Cass, which excited Polly's interest. She was even more intrigued when Cass, either attracted by Princess's swishing tail or anxious to detain his mother, caught her by her tail tuft and tried to hold on to it. Princess, however, does not like to have her tail bitten on, and freed herself quickly from her cheeky little son.

The goings on on Lion Island were by no means silent affairs. They were accompanied by calls, growls, and grunts. The cubs often made mewing noises, and sometimes even sounded like a nest of chirping little birds. Once I watched one of the cubs trying to catch up with the rest of the family. He uttered low growls as he ran as fast as his short legs permitted, and the sounds he made reminded me vividly of someone swearing under his breath. When Princess talked to her little cubs, she mostly made soft, almost moanlike sounds in a voice she never uses toward Charlie. One day Princess had disappeared from view for several minutes because she had taken a walk along the lower shelf of the island; Charlie, on looking about, did not see her and called out for her loudly. In reply,

Princess, looking sleek and trim, came rushing up from below and rubbed her
head lovingly against his, to his obvious satisfaction. As the cubs were not about
on that day, Charlie's call was undoubtedly meant for Princess alone.

When the cubs were less than three months old, the pace on Lion Island seemed to
quicken. Now both cubs followed Charlie's every move, and when he went over
to the scratching post, his youngsters accompanied him. Cass was very businesslike,
obviously determined to imitate his father's action, while Polly paid no attention
to it as she hugged her father's back.

As a lion cub learns by following its parents' example, it is important for it to be shown how to keep the claws in good condition. If these cubs had not lived in the middle of the Bronx Zoo, where meals are provided for them regularly, they would at this age also be shown by their parents how to hunt game. This is a skill our lions do not need. But they must learn how to exercise the muscles that control their claws. Lions, like all cats, are digitigrade : their sharp, curved claws are retractable and only bared to seize their prey. Anyone who observes the feeding of these cats will see that as soon as meat is offered to them, they use their claws to grab and hold it. This action, by the way, is sometimes accompanied by snarls and hisses, which seems to be a feeding reaction.

A few weeks later, Cass followed his sire to the scratching post every time he spotted him there, and the little cub imitating his father was a charming sight.

Even though her cubs were less helpless by then, Princess continued to be very protective. She has learned to ignore visitors watching from across the moat as long as they seem peaceful to her. But there are a number of circumstances she considers very threatening to her cubs : when someone tries to anchor a tripod with a long lens in the shrubbery that separates the public area from the edge of the moat ; when visitors hold children on their shoulders to give them an unobstructed view ; and when people carry flying balloons. She probably objects to these last two situations because these children as well as the flying balloons protrude above the normal level of peering faces that she has learned to tolerate. She once got so upset about balloons and children looking down from their parents' shoulders—sights at which she always snarls and spits—that she even growled at poor Charlie.

Having treated him unkindly seemed to upset her too, for she then took herself off to a more secluded corner next to the shelter house, turned her back to the crowd, and let Charlie do the baby-sitting for a while.

Charlie remained unruffled by Princess's outburst and his children's antics. Cass, at that age, had begun to play with his father more than he had done when he was smaller, but it was still Polly who was the more determined to get close to her

father. She liked to rest near to Charlie's head, moved her tail teasingly across his face when she passed him, and practiced climbing by scrambling up his back, while Cass was mostly anxious to ruffle his father's mane.

As the weather turned cooler and the cubs grew sturdier, the animals became even livelier. One day Princess chased Polly off Flat Rock, where the cubs had been playing, in order to sit on the rock herself in what looked to me like great dignity.

No sooner had she sat down than the cubs crept up after her and began playing around her. All of a sudden, Cass discovered his mother's tail tuft, and the inevitable happened—he bit on it, probably hurting her. Hence Princess got up, jumped down from the rock, and left it for her youngsters to play on while she found herself a more peaceful hideaway.

This was the first time that I saw Princess claim an adult's prerogative to a seat. I watched similar incidents a number of times with a later litter, when she hopped onto Flat Rock or Grandview and sat or stood on it for a while after a playful cub had gestured or called to her from it, trying to entice her to play or perhaps to roughhouse from that vantage point by waving its paw about and nudging her. Some of the cubs, particularly Cass, seemed to have a predilection for Flat Rock and enjoyed sitting on it, but none of these rocks seemed to have any attraction for Princess, and she never ousted a cub from them unless provoked.

As for Charlie, I have never seen him force a cub from a shady site that the adult might have fancied; in fact, I have never seen him show any tendency to make his family move for him. Apparently Lion Island provides sufficient shade, even in hot weather, to accommodate all of these animals. Charlie is unlike some of the short-tempered males whose descriptions you sometimes encounter in studies made in Africa, who will not permit the rest of the pride, except a favorite lioness, anywhere close to a comfortably cool area that they have claimed for themselves.

When the weather is cool, Charlie wants a workout for his energy from time to time. During the same period in which Princess chased Polly off Flat Rock, I saw Charlie crouching behind Grandview Rock to waylay Princess, who could not see him from where she was approaching. He jumped on her back, his forelegs around her shoulders, nipped her in the nape of her neck, and bowled her over, after which he nuzzled and licked her.

All set to ambush Charlie

Cass is inquisitive

Only Polly's tail and legs can be seen as Charlie spills her off his back

Several months later, I watched Princess reverse the game by ambushing Charlie one day when *he* did not expect this—except that she was somewhat crossed up by Cass, who, with the natural curiosity of a little cub, strolled over to take a look at what his mother might be up to. Despite this diversion, Princess sprinted to surprise Charlie, who, in his haste to get to his feet to meet the onslaught, spilled little Polly off his back.

Cass's and Polly's antics had become very amusing by the time they were about four months old, and they, as well as the previous and subsequent litters, have taught me that at an early age lion cubs seem to feel the need for greater independence from their mother. They indicated this obliquely but nonetheless clearly by their changed tactics. While Cass and Polly had previously tried to make their mother a partner in their games as much as possible, they now looked to their sibling for most of their entertainment. Their early explorations seemed to have been done at random, under Princess's watchful surveillance. Now however, they appeared to be quite deliberate in choosing amusements that would not alarm her and thus bring her to their side right away. They would, for instance, practice climbing on Flat Rock, an outcropping so low that neither parent saw a need for interference.

One day they were perched on Grandview when their mother walked by. She would undoubtedly have passed the rock without a glance at her cubs had it not

been for Polly, who waggled her little paw. This stopped Princess, who then gave her a few affectionate licks. The whole episode was reminiscent of children who think they have hidden so cleverly from the adults by just keeping out of their way and by not being spoken to, and at the end have to show mama how very smart they have been.

Yet a lion cub's urge for greater independence, and the fact that Cass and Polly no longer relied solely on mother as the only source of pleasure and amusement, should not be understood to mean that the cubs no longer wanted to play with their parents. Far from it. They had merely changed their approach. They now invited each other and their elders for a game in the same fashion as the adults: they indicated their willingness and interest by looking fixedly toward the other animal, by touching it with a paw, by a playful cuff, by running toward their parent expectantly; and the invitation was either accepted or rebuffed, or sometimes ignored.

Polly, however, continued to show her affection for Charlie whether
or not she was playing around him. On one occasion, the cubs were
engrossed in a game of something that looked like follow-the-leader
which took them past Charlie as he stood behind Flat Rock. As
Polly passed her father with Cass in close pursuit, Polly let her
little tail glide tenderly over her father's face.

Then something happened for which I was completely unprepared : submissive behavior by a cub toward its sire. Submissive behavior occurs among many animals, including most carnivores, and also herons, turkeys, and other birds. But it is practiced only between members of the same species. When a young animal is threatened by an adult or a weak one by a stronger opponent, he will show his helplessness and deference by rolling over on his back or by putting himself flat on the ground and extending his most vulnerable part, his neck, toward the would-be-killer. The dominant animal's instinct forbids him to bite a member of his own species as long as it remains in this attitude of humility.

It was a cool November day, and the adults had been very active chasing each other, frolicking, and racing about.

A cool day calls for strenuous exercise

This always seems to stimulate the cubs to greater activity, and when Polly saw
her father rush from the rocks in the back across the island, she jumped up on
her hind feet, looked toward him, and waved her forepaws about. Charlie must
have taken this for an invitation, for he raced straight toward her, and while at
first she had hopped about in what appeared to me to be great excitement and
anticipation, her imposing sire dashing toward her with undiminished speed
must have given her a real fright. She retreated very hurriedly as he approached
so fast, and seemed so intimidated and kept backing away toward the brink so
rapidly that with a sinking feeling I became convinced she was going to end up
in the moat, a sheer drop of some sixteen feet or so at that particular spot.
Princess and Cass must have been equally concerned : they both had very
anxious faces as they hurried toward Polly. By that time Charlie had drawn
up short beside his daughter, who had flattened out in front of him, very close
to the brink, in a completely submissive stance. He never touched Polly as
long as she remained flat on the ground. But when she got up, the other two
approached, and there was a great deal of moving about, of sniffing and licking
each other, of nuzzling and investigating, in which the whole family participated,
and it was a great relief to know that things had ended well, after all.

The crisp weather greatly stimulated the adults, and Princess and Charlie frequently engaged in a game that looked as if they might be playing tag. These games are probably a good outlet for their pent-up energy. Sometimes Princess started a rumpus by involving Charlie in a sham battle, running up to him and catching hold of his hind legs, which always brought him down and herself as well.

The cubs played often with each other's tails, and Cass continued his games with his mother's tail tuft. She did not like this any better in December than she had in the fall, yet she never reproved him. However, Princess took her revenge, in a way, by playing a game that she apparently enjoyed but her cubs did not care for: she frequently sat down on them, but was always very careful in putting her weight on her forefeet rather than resting it on her youngster. Nevertheless, both cubs always scrambled out from under her just as quickly as possible, and always voiced their protests. I have never seen her repeat this game with her third-litter cubs.

I was sometimes amazed to see Princess lying on her back, with her hind legs resting against Charlie's chest or shoulders. And while her mate was busy licking and caressing her, Princess cradled her little male in her arms, fondling and licking *him*.

A game that Princess often indulged in, and still does, is to plump herself down across Charlie's body while he is resting on the ground. Charlie appears to enjoy this too, for they then both roll about with their legs up in the air. This position encouraged his cubs to play with him one day. Both Polly and Cass approached their father and began to ruffle his mane and nibble on his elbow tufts. All of this must have been so pleasing to Charlie that he closed his eyes in bliss. When he finally sat up, Polly slid off his back and Cass urged him to continue with the game by nudging him with his paw. Apparently, Charlie had had enough. His cubs had not, however, and Cass tried to hold on to him with teeth and claws as Charlie walked away. Charlie just ignored these efforts.

Frequently when Charlie caresses Princess, the little cubs attempt in vain to remind him of their presence. Charlie then has eyes only for his mate and ignores his cubs completely. Not so Princess. With an ingenuity that some human mothers might envy, she manages to care for her young without ever neglecting her mate. One day, as Princess was lying relaxed on her back, her

cubs came to nurse. After a while, she apparently found the job of feeding her
children a bit monotonous, for little by little she inched closer to Charlie, who had
sat next to her all along but had shifted his position in the meantime. She
reached for him, and soon the lions were lying in a seemingly contented
if untidy heap, while Cass and Polly continued to suckle.

Another time I saw these lions in a wonderful ''pamper-dear-Charlie'' act, with Princess licking and grooming Charlie's face with complete concentration, Cass lying almost flat on his father's back, playing with Charlie's mane and nipping him occasionally, and Polly helping in this worthwhile endeavor. Charlie sat quietly throughout, only moving his head occasionally to give Princess better

access. A little later, the two cubs played near their sire, but this time Cass was
the one who wanted to be close to the big male, and began pawing his father's
mane, while Polly was busy nipping and licking her brother's hindquarters.
All of a sudden Charlie turned his head down toward Cass and spoke up

energetically; when he lifted his face again, he really looked disgusted—
apparently Cass had scratched and hurt him. But Cass, not the least impressed
by his father's protest and displeasure, ignored both completely and continued
blithely with his game, and gradually Charlie's facial expression returned
to normal. Throughout this episode he had remained in the same position
and had never made the slightest move to discipline Cass.

Princess frequently played with Cass, and when Polly became aware of these games, she would move closer to her mother, for undoubtedly she would have liked some more attention also, but I never saw her interfere in any of the games her mother played with the little male. They generally ended with Princess nursing both of her cubs.

As I watched the African Plains lions, I soon discovered that they kept much better track of the comings and goings of their keepers than I could. The slightest motion around the building near the bison range would make them shift their position to keep that area under careful scrutiny. They take a very lively interest in any kind of unusual occurrence where the Thomson's gazelles graze, and when the Nyala antelope buck mates with one of the females, all of the lion family troop over to observe. The wail of ambulances and fire engines often disrupts their activities, for they listen to these noises with great concentration.

As Charlie is even-tempered and not easily excited, he has at times deceived me into thinking that he was rather blasé. I have been cured of that notion, for even if, in typical lion fashion, he does not appear to take much notice of what goes on around him at times, nothing escapes his gaze. He is really quite inquisitive, as I discovered one day when he looked very puzzled. He craned his neck and finally got up to get a better view. When I turned around to look for the object of Charlie's curiosity, I discovered that one of the Zoo visitors carried his baby papoose-fashion in a sling on his back. Obviously Charlie had never before seen anything like this and had to have a good look so as to take it all in.

Observing lions is a fascinating experience, as these animals show a very high degree of variation in their different personalities. Each has its own preferences, its own ways of responding, and no two of them are alike. It has been fortunate that lion cubs, just like human children, seem to enjoy doing certain things over and over again once they have taken a fancy to a particular game. This sometimes gives the photographer a second chance, in case the first exposure did not come off. After studying these animals for some time and watching them quite closely, one can generally predict what they are about to embark on, from the way they move and look, and I would assume that this is how the members of a pride take their cues from each other. Lions are sociable animals; their faces betray their emotions, and their movements their intentions. Like all animals, they do not move about erratically but are quite purposeful in every one of their motions, so that their aims are made clear to whoever cares to be alert to these signs.

There was a hiatus of several months in my lion watching, because during the winter—unless the weather is mild, no ice sheets have formed on the island, and the moat does not hold too much water—the animals are confined indoors. In April 1964 I began to observe them again, but now refrained from photographing them except when some particularly appealing or unusual episode occurred.

The lion family

One day, when Cass and Polly were about ten months old, I was rewarded: Polly had followed Charlie to Flat Rock, and it was soon clear that she wanted to get close to him. She leaped onto the rock to be near him, then began fondling his

head and mane from that vantage point, and he, in turn, bent his head and rested it on the rock to make the approach easier for her. Finally she jumped down and turned around to him once again, and he extended an encouraging paw, probably

to invite her to continue—except that at this instant the other two members of
the pride approached and they all found something more exciting to do. A great
deal of frolicking went on that day. All four animals rolled on their backs,
pawing each other and enjoying themselves, and after Charlie caressed Princess,
as he so often does, she turned around to look at him while he still stood over her.

Everybody greeting everybody

Around that time, also, Cass showed the first signs of a growing mane, for there
were tufts of hair at the side of his neck, although there was not yet
a ridge of hair down his head and back. (The voices of the
cubs had long since acquired a more adult timbre.)

Not many weeks later, Polly developed a calcium deficiency that did not yield to
any treatment. When she died, everybody who had known her was much
distressed : she had become a real pet and was sadly missed. Cass, however,
thrived, and developed into a very endearing blond little male who
continued to greet his parents effusively at every opportunity.

RICHARD, ANNABELLE,
AND LUCY

It became apparent, early in April 1965, that new cubs were imminent, for Princess, normally so quick and vivacious, showed little inclination to move and also looked decidedly heavy. In line with the theory that a lioness generally has larger litters as she matures, and that her litters become smaller again when she grows old, Princess brought forth a litter of three on April 10, 1965. The cubs consisted of two females, named Annabelle and Lucy after two staff members of the New York Zoological Society, and a male, Richard (for Richard the Lion-Hearted).

Richard, Annabelle, and Lucy were two weeks old when I visited them in the shelter house to take their photographs while Princess was being fed in the adjoining cage. The little ones looked most appealing in their spotted, woolly coats, but appeared quite awkward as they crawled about on the straw-covered concrete floor. They were rather curious when Keeper Warren Lawston lifted two of them onto his knees, and they tried at once to explore his trousers. After a few minutes I heard a thud and, looking up, discovered Princess peering down on all of us. She must have become concerned about her cubs, jumped up to the sleeping platform of the cage she was in (producing the thud that I had heard), and from there had an unobstructed view of her cubs through the wire netting. She showed no sign of alarm, probably because she was used to having her cubs handled by Keeper Lawston, whom she had known for years and always trusted, and to whom she often showed her affection by coming close to the bars of the cage to greet him and have him pet her. Princess just stood up on that sleeping platform, looked down on her cubs, and called to them quite softly, *mhm, mhm, mhm, mhm.*

When I saw them again a week later, I was amazed at their rapid growth. They looked even more cuddly then, and after another week or so, their little teeth began to show in their mouths when they opened them to yawn or to utter birdlike chirps.

Richard, the largest of the cubs, gave the distinct impression that he enjoyed being held in his keepers' arms, for he never moved, let alone struggled, and at one time even seemed to go to sleep there. The littler of the two females, Lucy, did not mind being handled either, if it was only for a short period—otherwise she became restless. But her chubby sister Annabelle was quite shy and very nervous when picked up.

Annabelle (foreground), Lucy, Richard in the rear

Lucy

The little male had a dark line down his lower spine to the root of his tail, and Lucy had similar markings, although shorter and less pronounced. She also sported a cowlick in the middle of her spine. Annabelle's coat lacked such distinctive features. Her face appears rounder than Lucy's, which is heart-shaped. And while Richard used to have a full face like Annabelle's, now that he is about one year of age it is very much larger than his sisters', and he is also much bigger than they are.

Since those early days, the dark marks on Richard's and Lucy's coats have somewhat faded from view, but the camera will pick them up unfailingly and record them, just as it registers clearly the rosettes on Princess's coat.

When the cubs were from four to five weeks of age, they were taken by their keepers onto the meadow for short periods of time every day that the weather was fine, in order to exercise their little legs, as the concrete floor of the shelter house proved too slippery for them to gain proper purchase for their toes, and their gait had resembled a waddle.

Richard

During these excursions, Princess joined Charlie and Cass on the island, and there was a wonderful and tender greeting scene upon her reunion with the two males, after she had been cooped up indoors with her little cubs for several weeks.

Meanwhile the cubs had the time of their lives out on the meadow. They led keepers and curators a merry chase, for each of the little lions would take off in a different direction as soon as it was released from its keeper's arms. They explored each bush and each fence to see whether they could wiggle through or under it. They were greatly intrigued by the water in the pond, by wading birds and antelopes, and dashed hither and yon in great excitement and curiosity, hotly pursued by their keepers, of course, to keep them out of mischief. In fact they were so inquisitive that at one point the Zoo became concerned that if three grown-up men were needed to control the cubs on the meadow, perhaps Princess would not be equal to taking care of them all by herself on the island. Charlie could possibly be counted on to help, but his reaction to the new cubs was still untested. There was particular concern that Princess would be unable to prevent her cubs from falling into the moat.

Fortunately, it turned out that these worries were quite unfounded. Princess had no trouble at all in controlling her little ones when they made their appearance on Lion Island toward the end of May 1965. She kept them together by calling to them softly, and watched over them attentively as they explored their new territory.

It has been most interesting to observe the behavior of the cubs toward their parents, revealing their individual preferences. I had assumed that a female cub would favor her sire, the males would gravitate toward their mother, and that the adults would always prefer the cubs of the opposite sex. This assumption

turned out to be quite untrue. To the contrary, I have learned that lions are great individualists whose choices are just as unpredictable as man's, and easy generalization of their behavior will only lead to errors and misconceptions.

First of all, I would now hesitate to say that Princess or Charlie favor or favored any one particular cub. I wonder if they ever did. As mentioned before, Princess is an exemplary mother who watches solicitously over all her cubs. She will go over to them and lick and groom them meticulously every few minutes without playing favorites, and will play with any cub who wants a game. Charlie too will greet any of his cubs affectionately as they approach him, but from all I have observed, he is not the one who makes advances to the cubs.

It is the youngsters who play favorites. There can be no doubt about a cub's preference when you see him make a bee-line for his father at the first opportunity and cuddle up to him, or when you watch another cub running to her mother with insistent calls until she has reached her safely. Of course, the response that these cubs elicit from the parent they favor may lead the onlooker to feel that this cub is his parent's favorite. But a parental bias in favor of any one cub might be very difficult to prove.

As related earlier, the first- and second-litter cubs did indeed show the father-daughter and mother-son relationship. However, the third-litter cubs did not. From the beginning, Annabelle has been mama's little girl. One day in May, when the little cubs had been taken to the meadow for their practice walks, Annabelle was the one who led the way back to the shelter house and her mother, calling for her incessantly and loudly until she was reunited with Princess.

Annabelle's amazingly clear calls reminded me more of a tree frog's than of a small lion cub's. Annabelle's attachment to her mother has persisted, and there will be more about it in the following pages. Richard wanted to be close to his father all the time. He generally headed for Charlie as soon as Princess brought her babies out of the shelter house, and Charlie was very responsive to his little son: Richard most enjoyed snuggling under Charlie's chin. He was at times observed taking a snooze lying across Charlie's arms against his chest, or nibbling on Charlie's mane while hanging on to it with his claws, or edging close so that Charlie would lick him. He liked to rest on Charlie's back, and one day he surprised me by peering out from underneath his father's mane.

Lucy, on the other hand, seemed most devoted to her brother Richard with Charlie her second choice. She tagged after Richard all the time. She went over to Charlie, also, when she saw Richard there. Even without Richard she liked to nestle close to Charlie, but Richard was her principal playmate.

Richard and Lucy

This does not mean that the triplets did not get along or did not play with each other. Far from it. They had a wonderful time rolling around together, pawing and nipping each other, which gave their busy mother a bit of respite. Still she strode over to her little ones very often to lick them with great thoroughness.

At the end of May, when the cubs were about seven weeks old and out on the island with their parents for a few hours every day that the weather was good, I witnessed, for the second time, a lion cub's submissive behavior. The three cubs and their parents were assembled on the slope overlooking part of the moat and the west path that Zoo personnel use in order to get from one exhibit area to the other. Princess played with two of her cubs while Charlie looked on, and the third cub rested close by. All of a sudden this third little cub got up and ran across the island toward the shelter house, but well away from the dangerous edge. Nevertheless, as soon as Charlie spotted this, he got up and raced after the runaway, who, on hearing the big male approach, did not simply stop, as I had expected the youngster to do, but literally hurled itself into the air in a somersault of 180 degrees, to land on the ground with the head pointed toward its

Princess licks Richard, who is chewing on Lucy

father in a position of utter deference. So unprepared was I for this performance that I was unable to photograph the somersault and could only record what followed next: The cub cried while Charlie stood over his youngster as if he were a pointing dog; then the cub waved its paws about, got to its feet, and waited

patiently for Princess, who by that time had caught up with the two and first fondled Charlie before turning to her cub to lick her child like a good lion mother. This was also the first time I felt convinced that Princess's keeping her tail right on Charlie, as she reassured her cub, was no accident, and later events confirmed this.

No sooner were the third-litter cubs permitted on the island with their parents than they began their version of tail and tail-tuft hunting. Charlie, who seemed to be a target more often than Princess, found this particularly trying because there were now three, and not only two, frisky little cubs to contend with. In spite of this, I never saw Charlie strike back at a cub when it had hurt or molested him. He might speak up indignantly, but the cubs always ignored this, and when they became too annoying, Charlie got up and walked to a more secluded spot. During one of these incidents, I saw Lucy trying to play with father's tail tuft, which she

apparently felt sure she had captured when it flew up all of a sudden, to her immense surprise.

Princess continued to be highly alert to any dangers lurking about that might threaten her babies, and when she discovered some boys who had scaled the wooden palings close to the moat, and, of course, also very close to the island, she really grew frantic. But luckily, her keeper had noticed the boys about the same time she did, and chased them away.

Several weeks before, I had seen Princess race from one end of the island to the other in a state of utmost agitation, seemingly at a loss to figure out what exactly she had better do, when three boys vaulted the fence into the African Plains meadow that adjoins the island and is the playground for Nyala antelopes and wading birds. Fortunately, the boys climbed out again after crossing part of the meadow, and Princess's excitement subsided.

Another situation that was very upsetting to Princess when she first took Richard, Annabelle, and Lucy out on the island involved Cass. A lioness is very particular about the company her little ones may meet. Apparently the mate's presence is quite often acceptable to a lioness: there have been instances in other zoos, such as Maidstone, Dresden, and London, where lion fathers were left with their mates in one cage when the lionesses were about to give birth, and no accidents happened to the little cubs. In fact, the experiment at the Maidstone Zoo led its owner to believe that it might sometimes be beneficial not to separate the male from a young or nervous mother. But her tolerance of other male lions close to her cubs seems to depend largely on the individuals involved and on the personality of the mother.

I have read about two lionesses, both of them with cubs, who had teamed up together and who associated with two males, and the cubs were not hurt by these males. There is also a report that a two-week-old cub was once left with a whole group of twenty-month-old youngsters that belonged to another lioness, and no harm befell the baby. In the wild, when a lioness expects another litter, mostly about the time the cubs of the last one are between one and one-half and two years old, the prides seem to break up, and the youngsters often form new groups.

"Keep off my cub." Princess's face shows a "threat" expression

By the same token, lionesses in the wild often associate with other lionesses, and quite a disparity in the ages of the cubs belonging to each female has sometimes been noted. Observations on lions in Serengeti National Park indicate that prides may consist of several adult lionesses, their cubs, and also one, two or even three males. Sometimes these older cubs would nurse from the lioness who had had a recent litter, while their own mother had no longer any milk. As it can be assumed that the prides observed in these studies consisted of both male as well as female cubs, it shows how tolerant lionesses are in accepting the presence of cubs, both male and female, of other litters and different ages in their pride.

Princess had, of course, demonstrated quite clearly that she harbored no ill feelings against Cass, then about twenty months old, when she greeted him and Charlie so fondly shortly after the three new cubs were born and before she associated the island with her new babies. But as soon as the little cubs set foot on the island for the first time, Princess objected to Cass's presence anywhere near her little ones, and she became very aggressive toward him when the Zoo tried to get all of the animals out on the island together. The encounter had started auspiciously enough by Charlie walking toward his son and rubbing his head fondly against Cass as the latter emerged from the shelter house. Then one of the small cubs ran toward its older brother. This was when Princess began to interfere. She attacked and crowded Cass to such an extent—and Charlie, on seeing her reaction, took her side in this—that Cass fell into the moat, a very unhappy cub, and was even more upset when a peahen who had been brooding quietly in the jumble of vegetation in the moat flew off suddenly because the lion cub's unexpected appearance had startled her. Cass, who had never been in the moat before and did not know his way about, was so intimidated by all this that he had to be baited out of the moat and up the path that leads back to the shelter house.

Since that day Princess's reaction to having her older son mix with the little cubs was tested a number of times, but always with very negative results. After the last experiment, when Cass was again pushed into the moat, it took a very long time getting him back into the shelter house because the area where he had fallen is mostly covered by water. Although the water is no more than about half a foot deep and there is a stretch at the side where he could have walked dry-footed, he apparently did not dare move, so that Charlie was sent out to show his son how to get home. Charlie walked over to him, greeted him profusely, lion-fashion, then made a movement with his head, almost like a human being who wants to indicate "Come on," and strutted back, but Cass did not follow. Many hours elapsed before he finally made his way back to the house and his dinner.

The interesting new log

Since Princess will not tolerate Cass anywhere near her three cubs, he has, in Charlie's company, been taking turns with his mother and her latest litter in the use of the island.

Scratching posts have to be replaced from time to time, and therefore a log was placed on the island at the end of May 1965 to serve the same purpose. All of the animals raced to investigate this new equipment. So did Cass when he came out later. After satisfying his curiosity, Cass sat down to study the log for a while, perhaps even to guard it. Then he apparently decided that it was another toy, and began pulling it about very vigorously, in different directions, until he finally managed to carry it between his teeth. He began walking with it, then trotting, but now he was in trouble, for the log was long and started to swing, probably upsetting Cass's balance. So he put the log down—unfortunately on the slope toward the moat—and was most upset when it began to roll and finally bounded into the moat. He ran disconsolately up and down alongside the moat, looking at his toy now in the water, and was so agitated about it that even Charlie got up to take a look. But after a single glance Charlie evidently concluded that rescue was hopeless, and went back to where he had been resting. Since then, a much bigger log has replaced the lost one, and while Cass still manages to pull it about and haul it to various spots, it is too large and heavy for him to carry and so it has remained on the island over the months for everyone's benefit.

Lucy

During those spring days, the three cubs were very lively, played with one another, followed their mother around, and were most inquisitive. Lucy once used her father's back as a convenient observation post to gaze in fascination at a bird in the tree shading Flat Rock. The youngsters were not a bit deterred when their parents were preoccupied with each other, fondling, licking, and nuzzling, and passed continuously through the low arch formed by Charlie's and Princess's heads. Their strategy paid off, for they came in for some affectionate caresses too.

The cubs continued to play favorites in associating with one or the other of their parents, and by just glancing at who was playing with whom, you could generally pick out the individual cubs, even before you inspected them for proper identification. Of course, each one of the cubs seemed to have a favorite game, and knowing this helped also. Lucy still followed Richard around or settled down close to him, and Charlie continued to be her second choice when she wanted company. She seemed to enjoy nestling into her father's mane, and Charlie was equally responsive.

In contrast to the way he had handled his very first cubs when they were small, Charlie showed great physical restraint toward the youngsters of later litters. While the cubs always approached him freely and rubbed their bodies and heads against him (to which he invariably responded affectionately), Charlie never made a move toward his youngsters initiating such approaches. When the cubs placed themselves under their sire's chin or extended their little paws playfully toward his face, he frequently stooped to lick

Lucy bird-watching

Princess grooms Charlie while Richard rubs against him

Richard tries to hold on to Charlie

them; at times he would bend down to the cubs when they sat or stood close to him, vying for his attention as he walked past them; occasionally he would hold one of his babies with his large paw in order to give his child a good licking. This was about the extent to which he would go. When the babies used his body as a convenient playground, he never budged, and only his facial expression gave a clue to the way he felt about it. Even when Richard tried to obstruct his father's advance by jumping up, placing his forepaws on Charlie's shoulder, and holding on to his father's mane with his teeth, Charlie did no more than walk faster to escape this annoyance. Quite plainly, Charlie refrained from playing with his later cubs while they were small. When the cubs were about four months old, he seemed to lose some of this restraint.

One day Richard tried to attract his attention, and in response, Charlie extended his paw somewhat tentatively toward his little son, and later started to lick him industriously, while resting on his side. Lucy no sooner spotted Charlie licking Richard than she left Princess, who had been grooming her, went over to her father, greeted him fondly, was nuzzled in turn, and then settled happily close to father and brother.

On the same day there was an enchanting scene between Princess and Annabelle.
First Princess held Annabelle in her arms (Lucy walking across at that particular
moment disturbed neither of them), and a little later Annabelle began to display.
Various rituals, each characteristic of a certain species of animal and well
understood by its members, sometimes even by other animals, are called
"displays." They may occur in connection with a mating ceremony, such as
the ritual dances of cranes, but also as a manifestation of excitement, for which
the hooting, rising, running, chest beating, and throwing of objects by gorillas

might serve as an example. Or they may represent means of communication with another member of the species. Lions use this method to convey their needs to other lions. In the case of Annabelle, she must have felt a great urge for her mother's attention. So she settled close to her mother's flank, rocked and bounced on her back, and waved her legs about while Princess licked and fondled her and Richard and Lucy sat close by watching. A little later mother and daughter rested cozily together and finally went to sleep.

Around that time the cubs at last mastered Flat Rock, and Richard looked very comical when he made valiant and eventually successful attempts to join Princess and Annabelle, who were both peering over that rock from the other side. In fact, playing around Flat Rock became one of their prime amusements for a while, and the cubs looked particularly cunning when they got on their hind feet in the back of the rock and peeped over its top at Zoo visitors. A few weeks later, they also "conquered" Grandview Rock, and from then on they could often be found stretched out on either of these rocks, gazing at the goings-on about them.

Observation seems to be a very important tool for lion cubs to learn by, and it is triggered by the youngsters' great curiosity. The different litters of cubs have shown me that alert young lions are not at all bored observing the actions of their elders. They study every move very carefully, much as human children might watch a play or television performance, and one day these cubs will probably behave in a manner similar to their parents'. This was illustrated one very hot and sultry day during which Richard, Annabelle, and Lucy had rested quietly, quite obviously affected by the heat, when Princess and Charlie began playing with each other. Instantly, the youngsters became alert and interested in seeing the adults disport themselves.

But unless hampered by excessive heat and the resultant physical discomfort, the cubs had no trouble whatever in improvising their own games and amusing themselves with each other; the log originally placed on the island for the animals to sharpen their claws on became one of the cubs' favorite playgrounds. The other one remained Flat Rock, where Lucy often sat to serve as the pride's bird-watcher.

The cubs watch their parents as if they were performers in a play

Lucy bird-watching

Throughout the period during which I observed these animals, I watched to see if the parents disciplined any of their cubs. But I have never seen Princess in such action, although she often interfered with a cub when she considered it imperative for its safety. However, Mr. Davis has told me that he has seen her swat one of her cubs so as to make an order stick. I do remember the day that Cass passed the cage which held his mother and her newest cubs, at that time only a few weeks old. Cass became very excited, probably because it had been a long time since he had been close to Princess. (Lions are, after all, sociable animals.) Trying to get to her, he jumped up and clawed at the iron netting which separated him from her. Evidently concerned for the safety of her small cubs, Princess became equally excited, reared up on the iron netting in turn, and growled threateningly. Charlie, who had been released from his cage after Cass, in passing Cass gave him such a blow with his large paw that Cass fell from the wire netting and went out of doors with his father, a very subdued young lion.

With the advent of cooler weather, the adults once again became very active, and worked off their energy with strenuous games. Another outlet for their excess energy seemed to be their roaring. But as I have watched these animals over the years, I have also gained the impression that there must be a territorial significance to a lion's roar, and a number of observers in Africa have expressed similar views. When all of the lions join in this concert, Charlie beginning, Princess following, and Cass contributing to the chorus from inside the shelter house, Charlie and Princess frequently face in opposite directions while delivering these roars; also, Charlie often paces along the edge of his dominion, roaring away. At times the little cubs listened attentively to their elders, but not for long. I have watched them snuggle up to Charlie's face and fondle him while he carried on with the roaring completely oblivious of them.

Charlie and Princess roaring away

When Charlie is not preoccupied announcing to the world that he is the master of Lion Island, he seems to welcome it when a member of his pride comes to greet him, and he then always acknowledges these caresses. At times he takes the initiative, particularly if one of the animals joins the assembly after having been in the shelter house. But no matter how hard I have tried over the years to time these occasions—how long? how often?—and tried to establish which one of the animals might indulge in it more often or longer than another, I have been unable to find a pattern. All of these things seem to depend entirely on the animals involved, their moods at a given time, and the circumstances in which they find themselves at the critical moment.

That lions are individualists who do not necessarily adhere to typical behavior was demonstrated one day when Princess groomed Richard, who was sitting on Flat Rock holding a wooden stick between his teeth. Proper lion etiquette would have demanded that he reciprocate and groom his mother in return—in fact, she bent her head in anticipation. But Richard obviously felt that it was more important for him to hold on to his stick. His mother bore him no malice for this breach, and continued to fondle him.

Princess has over the years developed a highly personal use for her tail. When I first began observing the African Plains lions at the Bronx Zoo regularly, back in 1963, Princess never used her tail in any striking manner. She twitched it when she was annoyed, lashed it when about to charge, and pointed it up, stiffly, when she jumped. Since the middle of 1965, however, she has become very sophisticated in handling her tail, for she now manipulates it almost as if it were another limb with which to caress Charlie or at least keep in physical contact with him when she must step a pace or two away from him. Occasionally, some of the cubs had shown similar tail gestures—when Polly, the affectionate little female of the second litter, fondled her father in this manner, and when Richard, one day, curled his tail around Lucy while they were both walking together. Lately I have seen Lucy caress Charlie with her tail also.

The only other ''roaring'' cat I have seen who uses her tail in a similar fashion is Blackie, the lovely little black female leopard in the Zoological Park, who always fondles her mate with her tail while she demonstrates her affection to her keeper by trying to snuggle up to him, an action that makes her mate extremely jealous and brings forth threatening growls and snarls.

Richard's tail embraces Lucy

Princess continued to care for her cubs. One late afternoon that fall, the adults crowded into the shelter house as soon as the door was opened to admit them : they are usually much more anxious to get to their dinner than the cubs are. After a few playful dashes in and out of the house, the youngsters finally entered—all except for Lucy. Lucy had decided to go for a stroll around Lion Island while the family waited for the door to open, and when she reappeared she found them gone. Lucy walked across the island, looking for them, and finally sat down on the rocks far in the back, calling. The shelter house's outer door had remained open, but none of the animals came to search for her and Lucy continued to call. Knowing that Senior Keeper Roy Hosmer was alone on duty that evening, I walked over to the shelter house to inquire whether there was anything I could do to help. "No, thanks, nothing—but *where* is Lucy?" "Why, on the rocks in the back, shouting." "Oh, all right, I'll send Princess to get her." And so he did. Princess needed no instructions to tell her what to do. As soon as her keeper opened the inner door for her, she bounded out, walked across to her daughter, nuzzled her, and brought her back to the shelter house within a few minutes. I have been wondering ever since what prompted Lucy to stay out until Princess fetched her home, unless she continued to adhere to the cubhood rule that a youngster stay put at the place where it had last seen its mother.

Around the turn of the year, a very intriguing development took place in Charlie's relationship to his cubs.

For reasons that I can only guess, Charlie did not yet roughhouse with the cubs of the third litter. I am not sure what prevents a lion father from doing so. As intimated before, Charlie seemed quite inhibited whenever his youngsters wanted him to romp with them, and I assume that his exposure to several litters of cubs and Princess's example taught him that little cubs have to be treated gently. The cubs, at that stage of their development, did not seem to concur with his views on this subject and were quite determined to stimulate their sire to more active games —particularly Richard. Richard, being a little male, was by then much larger than his sisters, and he enjoyed a scuffle.

One day I watched Richard try to rouse his sire in order to play with him, an effort that was handicapped by the fact that Charlie wanted to sleep. However, this does not seem to put off a determined lion cub : Richard tapped his father on the nose, then on the face, until Charlie was aroused sufficiently to observe his little son, who waved arms and legs about in his efforts to get a rise out of his sire.

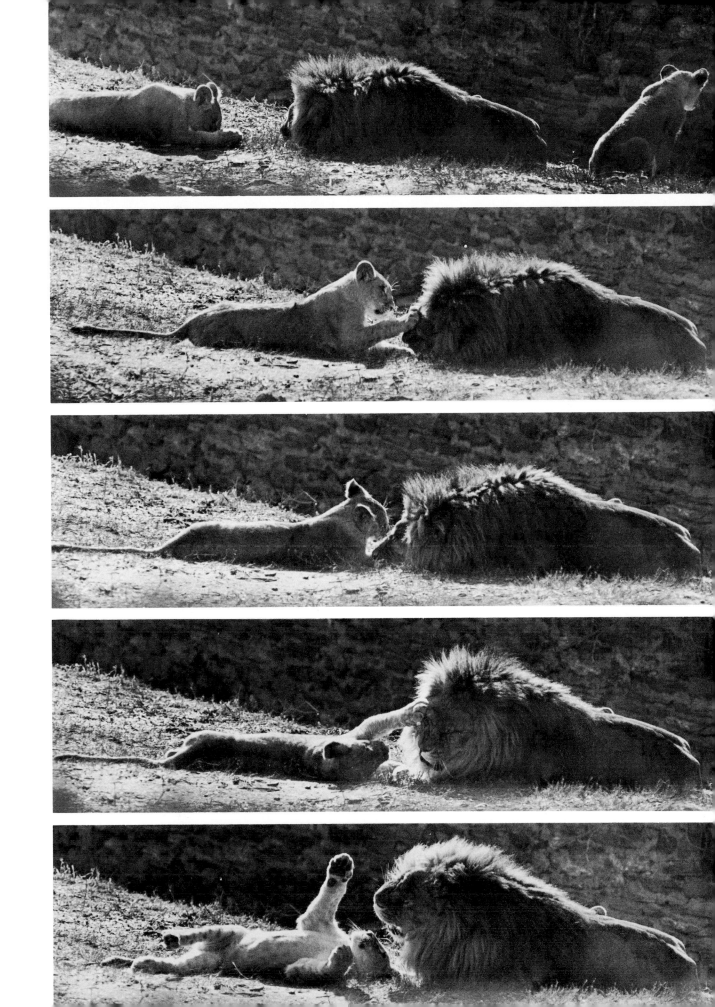

At last Charlie sat up and Richard promptly stood up against his father's back, nipped him, and ruffled his mane, so that finally Charlie turned around and got to his feet. Richard then threw himself on his back in front of his sire, ready for a tussle, while Lucy approached curiously to find out was was going on. Charlie gave his son a few pokes and cuffs—for which Richard had worked so hard—and played with him for a little while. Richard's attempting to wake his father up sufficiently for a game became a frequent occurrence.

Once in a while he was unsuccessful, and had to be content just to sit beside his dozing father, a very disappointed little cub.

Richard's performances for Charlie and Annabelle's displays for Princess are strikingly similar to those described by Eric F. V. Wells, a very well-known expert on the behavior of wild and tame lions, except that the antics described by him were carried out by lionesses to gain attention from the male. As our lion cubs have demonstrated, this type of behavior is probably inherent in the species, and when the urge for attention is strong enough, individual animals will exhibit it in different situations. Anyway, Princess does not seem in need of much display to attract Charlie. When she lies down near him and looks at him expectantly, this seems a sufficient inducement for him to come over to nuzzle and caress her.

During the same period, Princess gamboled and played with her cubs, and seemed much less inhibited than Charlie, but she too appeared to use less than her full strength when she danced around with them, dealing out blows.

Another time, Princess played again with Annabelle, holding her in her arms, and Richard eyed them. When Princess nipped her daughter, Annabelle pulled a terrible face and spoke up in protest, but she did not run away and recovered her composure very quickly.

In his games with Cass, the older cub, Charlie shows none of the restraints so apparent in his dealings with the latest litter. He plays rough, and so does Cass. Cass is a most appealing, very blond young lion, whose light-colored mane is quite a contrast to Charlie's dark one when they chase about together. On an unusually mild February day in 1966, when the frost had melted on the island, Charlie and Cass were permitted outside around noon.

They had probably waited for this moment with ever-growing impatience for many hours—they delight in being out of doors. I had never seen them as aroused. They raced at least ten times from one end of the island to the other, in great excitement, and stopped, each time, very close to the brink. They ran with such speed that I was unable to focus my lens except for one exposure that turned out to be blurry at 1/500th second. Finally there was a temporary halt, and Charlie walked over to the shelter house to listen for the noises from the rest

of the pride. He always does this when he is out of doors and the others are inside. Conversely, when Cass is locked in and Charlie, the third-litter cubs, and Princess have the island to themselves, Charlie will go over to listen for Cass. After Charlie had informed himself about his family, he and Cass resumed their play. They rolled on the ground, nuzzled and pawed each other, sunned themselves, and made the best of the rest of the day.

In summer 1966, while Princess was in season, Charlie showed yet another facet of his personality. All of a sudden he prevented Cass, now thirty-four months old and almost adult, from going out on the island with him, probably because Charlie now considered Cass as a rival. Animals, just like people, have ways in achieving their goals if they are determined enough and can get away with it, and for a while Charlie did. But then the Zoo wanted Cass back on the island, and when his son appeared outside, Charlie charged him. There was no way for the young lion to escape from his attacking father, and therefore Cass was forced to assume a submissive stance by rolling over on his back, which stopped Charlie's assault. But as soon as Cass was on his feet again, Charlie went for him anew, and Cass had to adopt a position of deference a number of times before his sire gave up fighting him and became reconciled to his presence on the island. They again spend part of the day together on the island, and their relationship is very cordial once more.

A PRIDE OF LIONS

This, then, is the story of one family of lions in captivity. No doubt, compared to the behavior of lions in the wild, some of their responses have become modified by the routine of living within the confines of a zoo. Among other things, life in a zoo means that they have never hunted for their food—in fact, were never shown how to hunt. Instead their dinner is served them regularly year in, year out, and during most of the day, time is their own. As a result, their social responses to each other may appear more pronounced than they would be if they lived in the wild, for their every waking hour in the zoo is predicated on their social ties. And yet, basically, these animals have the same general makeup and the same traits their wild cousins possess, and can, therefore, teach us a great many things about them.

If the African Plains lions of the Bronx Zoo had lived on the veld in Africa, they might never have had to face some of the personal problems they encountered on Lion Island. The island, while large enough for one pride, is quite confining, and the animals cannot get away from one another. Had they lived in the wild, Princess would probably have had no need to show such intolerance toward Cass. There, Cass might have moved off a little way when Princess first objected to his approaching her new cubs. But as the little cubs grew larger, she might have accepted his presence, as long as the cubs gave no indication by noisy complaints that he was too rough with them, the more so as Charlie enjoyed Cass's company. Charlie, too, might have displayed somewhat different behavior if he had been living in the wilds of Africa. First of all, he might not have stayed around with Princess all the time, as he is compelled to do on Lion Island.

Moreover, Charlie wants a little privacy from time to time and sometimes finds the demands of his lively family excessive. A male lion's need for greater solitude is well established. In the wild, male lions do not generally associate with lionesses and their prides all the year round. They do, however, frequently return to the same pride of lions or single lioness throughout the time they occupy the same territory. In the interim they may have some rather loose relationship with another male. But even during the periods in which they are members of a pride, they do not necessarily spend all their waking hours in as close proximity to the other animals as a place like Lion Island would compel them to. Charlie has proved to be an unusually placid, tolerant, and sociable male, but he, too, has an urgent need for privacy from time to time. I have seen him whirl around and tell

his family with an angry growl and a disgusted expression on his face that he wanted to be left in peace, after he had played with Princess and one of his cubs for an extended period. In the wild, Charlie would probably have simply strolled away to settle down at a distance, and he would have reappeared when he was ready for them once again. Also, Charlie would not have been impelled to fight Cass had they all lived in the wild. Charlie's attack on Cass was probably caused by his looking upon his son as a rival whom he had to prevent from associating with his mate now in season. In the wilds of Africa Cass, almost three years of age, would most probably by that time have left the parental pride to associate with other young lions, and might at his age have found himself his own lioness.

A pride of lions

There seems to be a striking disparity between some of the descriptions I have read and what I have observed on Lion Island on the often repeated statement of the laziness of lions. I have found little evidence of this as I have watched the animals on Lion Island, and I believe that this seeming contradiction has several causes:

First of all, in a surprising number of cases, it seems to be a matter of semantics: The writers frequently described an animal as ''lazy'' when it was unwilling to attack or otherwise get embroiled in a fight; also when a male partook of the kill another animal had made instead of going hunting for himself. By and large, lions are not aggressive animals, males even less so than females, unless provoked, driven by hunger, or in defense of their young and their territory. To call this characteristic or its ensuing consequences ''laziness'' is quite erroneous.

In the wild, lions feed rather irregularly; but when a kill has been made and meat is available, they often feast until they cannot hold any more food, then become extremely lethargic and will not budge until most of the food has been digested. Of course, it is a lot easier to encounter and observe a group of resting (lazy?) lions in the wild who, having gorged themselves a short while ago, do not want to stir, than to watch for any length of time animals on the move or prowling. Also, lions feel the heat a great deal and will try to spend the hottest hours as quietly as possible, resting or sleeping, but may become active toward the end of the day when the heat no longer bothers them—by which time a good many safaris will have returned, or be about to return, to camp.

Zoo lions, on the other hand, are not given enormous meals at irregular intervals that they have to sleep off for days. But in many zoos these animals have neither the space nor the motivation for exercise.

It is conceivable, of course, that the African Plains lions at the Bronx Zoo are unusually active creatures. Yet I have my doubts about this. I tend to believe that these animals, having lived on Lion Island since they were youngsters, are used to a more active life, and as they get a meal at the end of the day but not a particularly large one, they are inclined to be vivacious out of doors unless, of course, the heat troubles them too much. Besides, they do not have to conserve their strength and skill for hunting and yet need to release their energies in some way. This, coupled with the fact that they live in a family group that provides its own stimulations for play and exercise, very probably accounts for their liveliness and drive, as compared to animals that must spend their life in cages.

In closing, it might be useful to mention that when searching through the available literature on the behavior of these big cats, I frequently found one writer's conclusions contradicted by someone else's findings in some other study, although all of these writers are, or were, reputable naturalists. This surely is an indication of the variety of behavior these animals may exhibit, and Wells, an expert on lion behavior mentioned previously, is said to have summed up his views on this subject by stating that lions are creatures without rules and without exceptions.

I hope these pages will contribute toward a better understanding and appreciation of these wonderful animals, and serve to advance the cause for the protection of this now endangered species.

Lucy regards the world from a dependable vantage point

BIBLIOGRAPHY

ADAMSON, G. A. G. "Observations on Lions in Serengeti National Park." *East African Wildlife Journal,* August 1964.

ADAMSON, JOY. *Born Free.* New York: Pantheon Books, 1960.

————. *Living Free.* New York: Harcourt, Brace & World, 1961.

————. *Forever Free.* New York: Harcourt, Brace & World, 1962.

AKELEY, CARL ETHAN. *In Brightest Africa.* Garden City, N.Y.: Doubleday, Page & Co., 1923.

ANONYMOUS. "Zoo Stars: The Fifteen Lions." *Zoo and Animal Magazine,* Vol. I, No. 4, September 1936.

ASTLEY MABERLEY, C. T. "Lion Entertainment." *African Wild Life,* Vol. III, No. 1, March 1957.

BALDWIN, CAREY. *My Life with Animals.* Menlo Park, Calif.: Lane Book Co., 1964.

BERE, RENNIE. "A Lioness and Her Cubs." *Animals,* No. 6 (2) :29, 1965.

BIGALKE, RUDOLPH. "Bushveld Tragedy." *African Wild Life,* Vol. 9, No. 3, September 1955.

————. *Let's Visit the Kruger Park.* Johannesburg: Afrikaanse pers. Boekhandel, 1961.

————. "Lions in the Kruger National Park." *African Wild Life,* Vol. 8, No. 1, March 1954.

BOPP, PETER PAUL. "Schwanzfunktionen bei Wirbeltieren." Separatdruck aus *Revue Suisse de Zoolog.* Tome 91, Fasc., Mar. 1, 1954.

BREHM, A. E. *Tierleben.* 4. Auflage, edited by Prof. Dr. Otto zur Strassen, Leipzig: Bibliographisches Institut, 1925.

COOPER, JOSEPH BONAR. "An Exploratory Study on African Lions." *Group Psych. Monographs* Vol. 17, No. 7, Serial No. 9, October 1942.

COWIE, MERVYN. *The African Lion.* London: Arthur Barker Ltd., 1965.

CRANDALL, LEE S. *The Management of Wild Mammals in Captivity.* Chicago: University of Chicago Press, 1964.

————, with WILLIAM BRIDGES. *A Zooman's Notebook.* Chicago: University of Chicago Press, 1966.

DAVIS, JOSEPH A., JR. "Family Life on Lion Island." *Animal Kingdom,* Vol. LXV, No. 3, May-June 1962.

DENIS, ARMAND. *On Safari.* New York: E. P. Dutton & Co., 1963.

EDMONT-BLANC, F. *Mammalia, 1957.* No. 21 (4):452-453.

GERLACH, RICHARD. *Mein Zoobuch.* Rueschlikon-Zurich, Stuttgart, Wien: Albert Mueller Verlag, 1959.

GROMIER, EMILE. *La vie des animaux sauvages de l'Afrique.* Paris: Payot, 1936.

GRZIMEK, B. and M. *Serengeti darf nicht sterben.* Berlin-Frankfurt-Wien: Ullstein Verlag, 1959.

GUGGISBERG, C. A. W. *Simba, the Life of the Lion.* Philadelphia: Chilton Books, 1963.

————. *Unter Loewen und Elefanten.* Bern: Hallwag, 1953.

————. *The Wilderness Is Free.* Cape Town: H. Timmins, 1963.

HECK, LUTZ. *Tiere—mein Abenteuer.* Wien: Ullstein, 1952.

————. *Grosswild im Etoschaland.* Berlin: Ullstein, 1955.

HEDIGER, HEINI. *Exotische Freunde im Zoo.* Basel: F. Reinhardt, 1949.

————. *Wildtiere in Gefangenschaft.* Basel: B. Schwabe & Co., 1942.

————. *Skizzen zu einer Tierpsychologie im Zoo und im Zirkus.* Stuttgart: Europa-Verlag, 1954.

HUBBARD, W. D. *Ibamba.* Greenwich, Conn.: N. Y. Graphic Society, 1962.

IVY, R. HEWITT. "Lions Kill Only to Eat." *African Wild Life,* Vol. 7, No. 3, September 1953.

JEAREY, BERTRAM F. *Pride of Lions.* London: Longmans, Green & Co., 1936.

JOHNSON, MARTIN ELMER. *Over African Jungles.* New York: Harcourt Brace, 1935.

————. *Lion.* New York, London: G. P. Putnam's Sons, 1929.

————. *Safari.* New York, London: G. P. Putnam's Sons, 1928.

KUHNERT, WILHELM. *Im Lande meiner Modelle.* Leipzig: Klinghardt & Biermann, 1923.

LORENZ, KONRAD Z. *Man Meets Dog.* London: Methuen, 1954.

MEYER, ADOLF BERNHARD. "Bis wie weit in der historischen Zeit zurueck ist der Loewe in Griechenland nachweisbar?" Sonderabdruck aus *Zoologischer Garten,* J.44, 1903, pages 65-73.

MOOREHEAD, ALAN. *No Room in the Ark.* New York: Harper, 1960.

PIENAAR, A. A. *The Adventures of a Lion Family and Other Studies of Wildlife in East Africa.* London: Longmans, Green, 1923.

ROEDELBERGER, FRANZ A., and GROSCHOFF, VERA I. *African Wildlife.* New York: Viking Press, 1965.

SCHALLER, GEORGE B. *The Year of the Gorilla.* Chicago: University of Chicago Press, 1964.

SCHULTHESS, EMIL. *Africa.* London: Collins, 1960.

SCOTT, JOHN PAUL. *Animal Behavior.* Chicago: University of Chicago Press, 1958.

SMYTHE, R. H. *Animal Vision.* London: Herbert Jenkins, 1961.

SPINAGE, C. A. *Animals of East Africa.* Boston: Houghton Mifflin Co., 1963.

STEVENSON-HAMILTON, J. *The Lowveld, Its Wildlife and Its People.* London: Cassell, 1929.

————. "Lions, as I Knew Them." *African Wild Life,* Vol. 1, No. 1, October 1946.

————. *Wildlife in South Africa.* London: Cassell, 1947.

SWANEPOEL, P. D. "The Disappointed Lion." *African Wild Life,* Vol. 10, No. 4, December 1956.

TYRWHITT-DRAKE, SIR GARRARD. *Beasts and Circuses.* Bristol, England: Arrowsmith, 1936.

————. "How to Raise Lions." *Animal & Zoo Magazine,* Vol. 2, No. 9, February 1938.

WELLS, ERIC F. V. *Lions Wild and Friendly.* New York: Viking Press, 1934.

WENT, ARTHUR E. J. "Breeding of Lions in the Dublin Zoo 1957-1962." *Science Proceedings Royal Dublin Society,* Ser. B 1 (8):67-81, July 1963.

YLLA, with L. S. B. LEAKEY. *Animals in Africa.* New York: Harper, 1953.

A NOTE ABOUT THE PHOTOGRAPHS

The photographs in this book were chosen from well over three thousand exposures. Sometimes it was impossible to obtain good photographs because of haze or poor light; sometimes the animals kept too much in the background for strong pictures; at other times they were not in the mood to be active. The animals were observed a great many more times than they were photographed.

All of the photographs were taken with a Nikon F camera, generally with a 135 mm 3.5 lens, on Kodak Plus X or Tri-X films, most frequently with an exposure of 250th second. The custom laboratory Axel Grosser, Inc., took care of the processing of the films and printing of the photographs. Their contribution to this book is gratefully acknowledged.

LIST OF DATES ON WHICH PHOTOGRAPHS WERE TAKEN:
  (*A slash / between two page numbers indicates a two-page spread.*)

Page 2	September 19, 1963	
Page 3	January 1, 1966	
Page 4-5	September 28, 1963	
Page 6	October 5, 1963	
Page 7-8	September 28, 1963	
Page 10	April 22, 1962	
Page 12/13	October 5, 1963	
Page 14/15	September 19, 1963	
Page 16/17	September 19, 1963; November 28, 1963	
Page 18-20	September 19, 1963	
Page 21	October 5, 1963	
Page 22	September 19, 1963	
Page 23	November 28, 1963	
Page 24/25	December 1, 1963; October 14, 1963	
Page 26-27	October 26, 1963	
Page 28	December 1, 1963	
Page 30	October 26, 1963	
Page 31-33	October 19, 1963	
Page 34-35	October 20, 1963	
Page 36/37	June 13, 1964	
Page 38-53	November 28, 1963	
Page 54/55	November 28, 1963; December 1, 1963	
Page 56-59	December 1, 1963	
Page 60-63	May 17, 1964	
Page 64	June 13, 1964	
Page 67	May 15, 1965	
Page 68	May 15, 1965; May 22, 1965	
Page 69	May 15, 1965; May 16, 1965	
Page 70	May 15, 1965	
Page 71	May 31, 1965	
Page 72	May 31, 1965; June 6, 1965	
Page 73	May 30, 1965	
Page 74	May 30, 1965	
Page 75	May 22, 1965	
Page 76/77	May 31, 1965	
Page 78/79	June 6, 1965	
Page 80	August 29, 1965	
Page 82-83	May 31, 1965	
Page 84	June 6, 1965	
Page 85	June 6, 1965; May 31, 1965; June 6, 1965	
Page 86-89	June 19, 1965	
Page 90	June 12, 1965	
Page 91	June 26, 1965	
Page 92	October 2, 1965	
Page 93	August 29, 1965; December 18, 1965	
Page 94/95	November 14, 1965	
Page 96	December 18, 1965	
Page 97	November 14, 1965	
Page 98	November 28, 1965	
Page 99	December 18, 1965; October 2, 1965	
Page 101-104	November 28, 1965	
Page 105	January 1, 1966; February 12, 1966	
Page 106/107	*Top:* September 5, 1965; *bottom:* February 12, 1966	
Page 108	November 14, 1965	
Page 110	December 18, 1965	
Page 111	January 1, 1966	
Page 112	December 18, 1965	
Page 113	December 11, 1966